# I Will Always Love You

By: Dr. Brie Turns

Illustrated By: Lisa Rasmussen

Publisher's Cataloging-in-Publication Data

Names: Turns, Brie, author. | Rasmussen, Lisa, illustrator.
Title: I will always love you / by Brie Turns; illustrated by Lisa Rasmussen.
Description: Chandler, AZ: Brie Turns, 2020. | Summary: As momma giraffe meets her new baby, she tells a sweet story of all the ways she will love little one throughout their lives.

Identifiers: LCCN: 2020906083 | ISBN: 978-1-7348543-0-5 (Hardcover) | 978-1-7348543-2-9 (pbk.) |978-1-7348543-1-2 (ebook)
Subjects: LCSH Giraffe--Juvenile fiction. | Babies--Juvenile fiction. | Mother and child--Juvenile fiction. | CYAC
Giraffe-Fiction. | Babies--Fiction. | Mother and child--Fiction. |
BISAC JUVENILE FICTION / Animals / Giraffes | JUVENILE FICTION / Family / Parents | JUVENILE FICTION / Family / New Baby
Classification: LCC PZ7.1 .T925 2020 | DDC [E]--dc23

Dedicated to:
Mckinley, I will always love you.

My Mother, thank you for always loving me.

The day I first met you,
the sun was shining brightly.

You looked up at me
and I smiled. I think
you smiled, too.

5

As I look down at you, I can already imagine
the wonderful life you will have.

You will go on adventures
to find hidden treasures...

Perhaps you'll explore the world
to discover new places.

But if you get scared or worried, remember —

I will always be here for you.

You will spend days playing and singing,
laughing and smiling, learning and growing.

But if it starts
to rain and gets
really scary,
remember—
I will always
protect you.

13

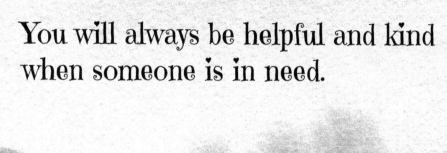

You will always be helpful and kind
when someone is in need.

But if life gets hard,
as it sometimes does,
remember...

16

I will always
help you.

Before you know it,
you will run off
and make new friends.

But even if it feels like I am far away, remember—

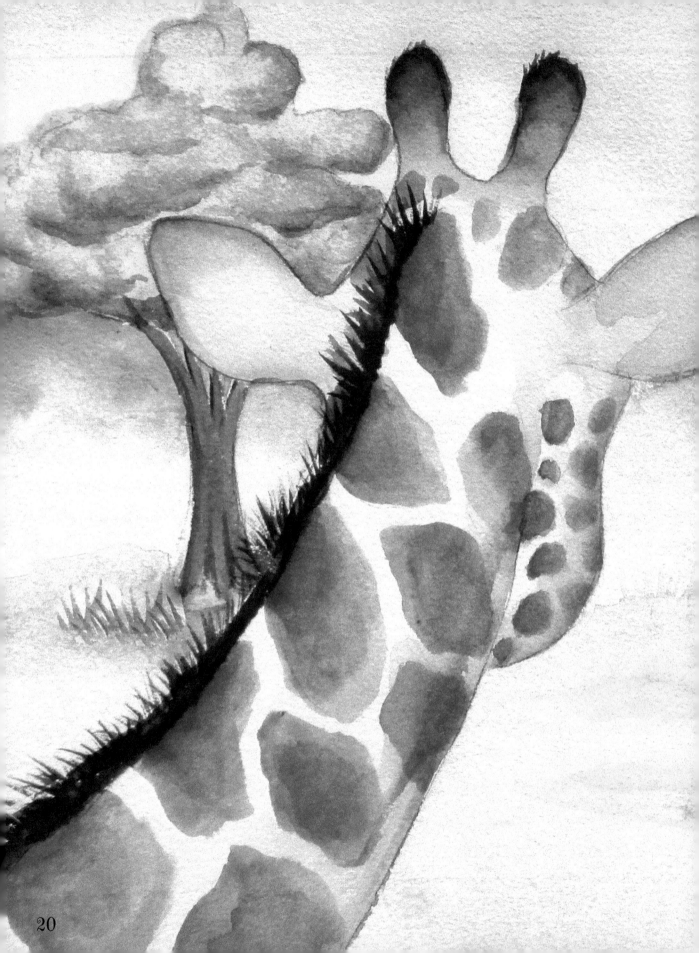

I will always comfort you.

You will grow bigger,
maybe even
bigger than me.

You will be able to reach up high.
Perhaps one day you will even touch the sky.

But if you ever get tired and need to rest,
remember—I will always rest with you.

Some day you will start a new life.
You will be busy with a family,
or even a baby of your own.
But even if I am far away, remember—

I will always be thinking of you.

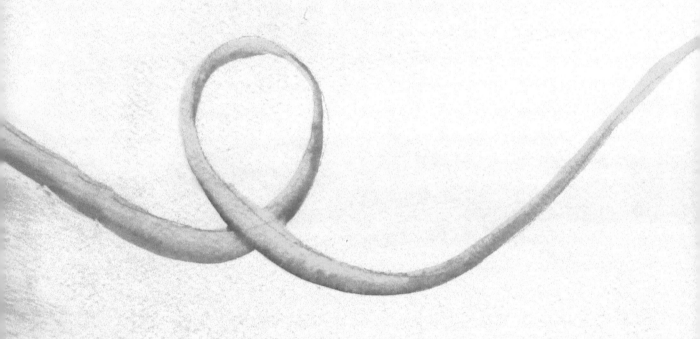

Be brave, my bright
Little One.
You will make a life
that is wonderful.

But no matter what happens, remember—

I

will

ALWAYS

love you.

# Dr. Brie Ann Turns

## Author

Dr. Brie Ann Turns is an assistant professor of Marriage and Family Therapy and a licensed associate of marriage and family therapy. She has previously taught at Purdue University-Northwest, Texas Tech University, and Lubbock Christian University. Dr. Turns currently teaches at Fuller Theological Seminary-Arizona.

Dr. Brie has spoken at local, state, national, and international conferences regarding families raising a child with an autism spectrum disorder. She has published numerous articles, book chapters, and magazine articles on various topics within the field of family therapy. Finally, Dr. Turns has been invited to speak at various universities including Yale, Brigham Young University, the University of Louisiana-Monroe.

# Lisa Rasmussen

### Illustrator

I hadn't planned on being an artist. I grew up on a family dairy farm with 6 other siblings in the foothills of Mount Rainier. Drawing and painting always came easy so I went to college to get a degree in Food Science and Nutrition and after working in the field for a couple years and being stuck in a lab I took my hobby and made it a business.

I try to give the animals personalities in my paintings and sometimes put them in humorous situations. There is so much love, emotion, and the gentle nature of the animals that I try to portray in my art. I started out with cows and farm animals but now I have almost every animal covered.

I am always working on something new and my customers, 3 kids and now 3 grandkids give me inspiration. I hope they bring a smile to you and to all that share them.

# Thank you for reading!

To download supplemental coloring pages so you can enjoy quality coloring time with your child, please go to www.thefamilytherapist.org/i-will-always-love-you

If you enjoyed this story, please consider leaving a review on Amazon or Goodreads to spread the word.

Printed in the USA
CPSIA information can be obtained
at www.ICGtesting.com
LVHW072159261023
762306LV00010B/31

9 781734 854305